50
COMMON EDIBLE & USEFUL PLANTS
OF THE SOUTHWEST

D1603389

David Yetman

WESTERN NATIONAL PARKS ASSOCIATION
TUCSON, ARIZONA

WARNING: *Wild plants make up a significant portion of the diversity of life. Many have also evolved ways to protect themselves against animals, including humans. It is against the law to disturb or collect plants located in protected public lands, such as national parks. Collecting and using wild plants may also cause you serious injury. The publisher and author accept no responsibility for injuries or damages you may receive while acting upon or using the contents of this publication.*

The net proceeds from Western National Parks Association publications support educational and research programs in the national parks. Hundreds of Western National Parks Association publications and products can be ordered online by visiting www.wnpa.org.

ISBN: 978-1-58369-106-9
Written by David Yetman
Edited by Melissa Urreiztieta
Designed by Campana Design
Cover photograph: *Yucca* spp. by Scott T. Smith
Illustrations by Brian Wignall
Map by Paul Mirocha
Printed through P. Chan & Edward, Inc.
Printed in China, 2012

Early in my studies among native peoples of southern Sonora, a friend pointed out a fruit the size of a small cherry that grows on a diminutive tree called the *pisi* (*Randia thurberi*, Rubiaceae). A small wasp finds this fruit much to its liking and deposits its larvae beneath the fruit's leathery husk. As the pulp of the fruit develops, the larvae consume it. Woodpeckers, with their marvelously sensitive hearing, detect the larva's presence and chisel out a hole, extracting the delectable grub. When the fruit dries, children pluck the now-hardened, hollow balls and blow forcefully across the hole left by the woodpecker, producing a piercingly loud whistle audible for a great distance. That knowledge is part of *ethnobotany*—the study of how people incorporate plants into their lives.

Engelmann's
hedgehog cactus

Larry Ulrich

Ethnobotany combines ethnography, the study of human cultures, with botany, the study of plants. Ethnobotanists study the plants people use for themselves and their communities. These studies may be simple (a short list of plants and their edible and medicinal uses in one's hometown, for example), or rigorous and challenging (such as a chemical analysis of plant combinations used to induce hallucinations and a physiological study of the neural and chemical pathways affected by the alkaloids in the hallucinogenic plant). Uses of plants include not only such obvious things as food, medicine, and firewood, but also less obvious things such as religious, industrial, artisanal, and cultural applications.

WHY PLANTS ARE USEFUL

Plants often evolve in ways that take advantage of how people and animals use them. We are fond of fruits for their taste, which is just fine with the plants. When their fruits appeal to frugivores, plants have enlisted natural allies for dispersion of their seeds, which for us are mostly indigestible. The more attractive the fruit, the higher the likelihood that creatures like us—or bats, doves, foxes, raccoons, or coyotes—will eat them and disperse the seeds. Some seeds, like those of some squashes and the chiles of the nightshade family, germinate more readily when they have passed through a digestive system.

Creosotebush flowering

Rick and Nora Bowers

We also find the leafy greens of some wild plants tasty when they are young and tender, but when the plants go to seed they tend to become tough and unpalatable to us. That suits the plants, since if we were to eat them during seed production we would grind up or digest many of the seeds and thus defeat the plants' reproductive strategy. An example of a plant's seduction, then repulsion, is the common Russian thistle, or tumbleweed (*Salsola kali*, Chenopodiaceae). As a very young plant its green shoots have a delicate flavor, quite at home in a salad. As a hardened old-timer brimming with seed, the tumbleweed is a harsh plant covered with many thousands of potent and irritating stickers.

For thousands of years humans have also been exploiting chemicals produced in plants to cure infections, alleviate the symptoms of disease, heal broken bones, expel parasites, prevent illnesses, promote or prevent pregnancy and childbirth, and induce altered states of mind. For eons people have made teas, potions, poultices, lotions, hot packs, porridges, smoking materials, and pomades to treat bruises, sprains, breaks, fever, pain, and swelling, and to promote pleasurable sensations.

In addition to food and medicine, humans use plants for constructing shelter and enclosures; for fabricating tools, toys, and weapons; for manufacturing paints, dyes, explosives (gunpowder requires charcoal), and other chemicals; and for cultural paraphernalia such as musical instruments, masks, and talismans.

ETHNOBOTANY IN THE SOUTHWEST

Plants of the Southwest evolved to tolerate drought and extreme temperatures, which provides them with properties often lacking in plants in more temperate climates. The diversity of southwestern plants is paralleled by the variety of indigenous peoples, unequalled anywhere else in North America. This seems odd, since many parts of the arid Southwest seem inhospitable places to live, but by exploiting the richness of plants, peoples of this region have managed to survive against great odds. Over the last couple of centuries, ethnographers have recorded ethnobotanical information from many southwestern groups: Akimel and Tohono O'odham, Apache, Cocopah, Eudeve, Guarijío, Hopi, Hualapai, Maricopa, Mayo, Mohave, Navajo, Seri, Yaqui, Yavapai, Zuni, and many more. These studies reveal an intimate connection between people and the plants that grow on the land where they live.

ABOUT THIS BOOK

In this book I have selected fifty plants of the Southwest that native peoples have found useful. Common names vary from one place to another, so to avoid confusion it is helpful to refer to a plant by its scientific name. Many of the plants in this book are common, while others are seldom seen. Some annuals appear only after rains and are then absent for long periods. Even perennial plants may be almost unrecognizable during droughts, but with a few summer showers they are transformed and recognizable.

In many places throughout the Southwest, the National Park Service preserves habitats where these plants grow. Many park service sites also interpret the traditional uses of plants by indigenous peoples, and some even maintain ethnobotanical gardens on-site that feature selections of native plants with edible and medicinal properties.

Please combine the information in this book with a respect for the land on which the plants grow. Do not collect any plants or plant materials without first obtaining permission from the landowner. Collecting materials of any kind is expressly forbidden on lands administered by the National Park Service, most state trust lands, and on tribal lands. If the land in question is managed by the U.S. Forest Service or Bureau of Land Management, collecting anything other than token amounts requires a permit. Most state, county, and city parks forbid the removal of any materials.

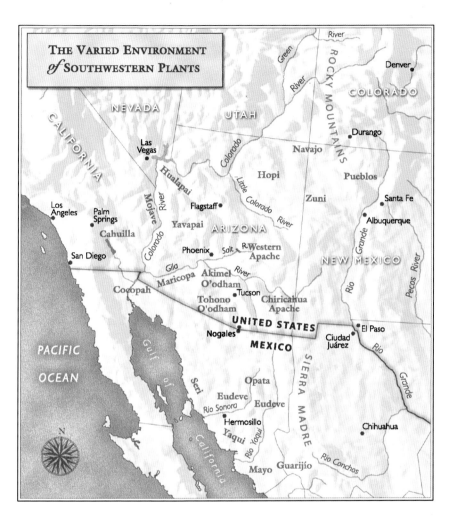

THE VARIED ENVIRONMENT
of SOUTHWESTERN PLANTS

River

Green

River

ROCKY MOUNTAINS

Denver

COLORADO

NEVADA

UTAH

Durango

CALIFORNIA

Las
Vegas

Colorado

Navajo

Hualapai

Little Colorado

Hopi

Pueblos

Los
Angeles

Palm
Springs

Flagstaff

Zuni

Santa Fe

Yavapai

ARIZONA

Colorado River

River

Albuquerque

Cahuilla

Mojave River

Rio Grande

San Diego

Colorado

Phoenix

Salt

R.Western
Apache

NEW MEXICO

Gila

Pecos River

Cocopah

Maricopa

Akimel
O'odham

River

Rio Grande

Tohono
O'odham

Tucson

Chiricahua
Apache

UNITED STATES

El Paso

Nogales

MEXICO

Ciudad
Juárez

Rio

PACIFIC

Gulf of

SIERRA

Grande

OCEAN

Seri

Opata

MADRE

Eudeve

Rio Sonora

Eudeve

California

Hermosillo

Yaqui

Chihuahua

N

Rio Yaqui

Mayo

Guarijío

Rio Conchos

Rio

Please note that plants with toxic or harmful properties often closely
resemble harmless ones. Although most plants can be examined without
fear, tasting plant parts can be hazardous or even lethal. Unless you have a
seasoned familiarity with plants of the Southwest, it is a good idea to treat
all parts of them as potentially poisonous.

I wish to draw attention to the Suggested Reading at the end of the book.
I have learned from all of these sources in addition to the indigenous peoples
of the Southwest who have shared their knowledge with me. These books are
all valuable sources of information and essential for anyone wishing to learn
more about the ancient relationship between people and plants.

1 · Agave
Agave spp.

FAMILY	Agavaceae
OTHER NAMES	century plant, *maguey, mescal, lechuguilla*
RANGE	throughout the Southwest
USES	food, fiber, medicine, beverage

Larry Ulrich

A gaves, or century plants as desert old-timers call them, make up a varied and most useful genus. Agaves range from sea level to more than 7,000 feet in elevation. Their size ranges from rosettes a few inches across and about the same height to monstrous plants well more than 10 feet tall and equally wide. Before it dies, an agave sends up a shoot or stalk that may exceed 20 feet in height. Most agaves have very stout and often viciously sharp leaf tips and may sport barbs along the leaf margins. They are closely related to the lily family, however, and only distantly related to cacti.

For thousands of years, humans have used agaves for making alcoholic beverages, food, glue, medicine, paper, and soap. From the fibers people wove rope, belts, garments, containers, and mattresses. The plants' dried stalks serve as handy poles. In my house, the dead stalks left with their dried flower capsules intact make perfect Christmas trees. Agaves are important horticultural plants as well. In my yard I usually have around fifteen species. In nature, agaves play a central role as food for bats and other creatures that in turn pollinate agave flowers.

While agaves are now best known as the source of tequila (from the stems or bases of *Agave tequilana*), distilled beverages were unknown in pre-Hispanic America. Before the arrival of Europeans, indigenous peoples produced a variety of fermented drinks. The best known is *pulque* from central Mexico, the fermented juice of *Agave salmiana*. At least 9,000 years ago native peoples discovered that the thick stem and leaf bases of some agaves, when pit-roasted, yielded a delicious and healthful food, one that could sustain people for long periods of time. We know the antiquity of agave use by the discovery of semi-fossilized *quids*—remnants of agave fibers that were chewed and spat out—whose age is revealed by carbon-14 dating. We know from current uses that agave blossoms are edible as well.

Agave murpheyi is especially important in the prehistory of the Southwest. Its use has been so widespread over millennia that its place of origin is unknown, though today it is found from desert areas of northwestern Sonora well into central Arizona. Native peoples planted it extensively, apparently impressed with the ease with which it would take root and the excellence of its roasted stem and leaf bases. *A. parryi* is another species prized as food. It prefers somewhat higher elevations and constituted an important dietary basic for Apaches. It is also a most handsome addition to one's yard. *A. chrysantha* and *A. palmeri* are common agaves used as food sources as well.

To roast an agave, the preparer usually selects a plant that is about to send up a shoot, lops off the leaves, and pries it from the ground (the roots are shallow). The stem (called a *cabeza* or *piña* in Spanish), whole or chopped, is placed on hot coals in a roasting pit, covered, and left to cook for a day or two. When it is done roasting, the leaf bases and parts of the *cabeza* are heavy with a rich, very sweet molasses flavor that is surprisingly filling and nutritious and can be stored indefinitely.

To make distilled agave liquor, harvesters cut the youthful stalk off just where it is about to emerge from the base. After enough time has passed—a few weeks to more than a year—the moonshiner uproots the plant and cuts off the leaves and roots, chops the *cabeza* into small pieces, roasts it, and tosses it into a tank where fermentation begins. Repeated distillation of fermented *cabezas* yields a potent, clear liquid.

The age of an agave when it sends out a shoot and dies varies greatly, but is far less than a century, usually ten years or fewer. The leaf juice from many species is irritating to the skin and may cause blisters.

Bruce Griffin

2 · Amaranth
Amaranthus palmeri

Although the tiny amaranth seed has been an important source of starch and protein for millennia, the plants are best known in the Southwest as a source of fresh greens. After abundant thunderstorms in July, amaranths (called *bledo* in Mexico) sprout from the ground as if by magic, especially on disturbed soils, sometimes covering many acres with countless thousands of plants. These tender shoots taste rather like spinach when steamed or boiled. Many native cooks sauté them with onions and garlic and perhaps a little chile.

One has only a few days to gather the young plants. They are in a rush to put out seed, just in case the rains stop, so when they are only a few inches tall they send out a flowering shoot and rapidly begin to lose both their flavor and texture. By the time the seeds begin to mature, the plants are tough and inedible and the seed heads are covered with stickers that produce nasty itching and swelling in many people. Seeds from these irritating stalks were an important source of grain for many groups. Women had the unpleasant task of gathering the seed heads, then beating them to loosen the seeds and winnowing what they collected.

If July or early summer rains fail, seeds may not germinate and no amaranth crop will be available. This is one reason why the summer rains have been of such importance to native peoples of the Southwest.

Debra Valov

FAMILY	Amaranthaceae
OTHER NAMES	pigweed, careless weed, *bledo*
RANGE	throughout the Southwest
USES	food

3 · Arrowweed
Pluchea sericea

Wendy Hodgson

Along the Colorado River this straight-branched plant often exceeds 10 feet in height and grows by the millions in nearly pure stands. *P. sericea* flourishes in similar habitats throughout the southwestern United States. Arrowweeds can tolerate alkaline soils, where they seem to prosper. So abundant and prominent is the plant in the lower Colorado region that Mexicans refer to residents of the desert city of Mexicali, Baja California, as *cachanillas*, after the Spanish name for arrowweed. The flowers are pinkish, the stalks covered with fuzz, and the long, narrow leaves are reminiscent of willows.

Arrowweed was one of the most-used plants of southwestern river peoples. They harvested the stalks in huge quantities without making a dent in its populations. Both stalks and branches are arrow-straight, making them ideal for, well, arrows, which Colorado River peoples used with deadly effectiveness against Spanish invaders. The stalks are also as useful as bamboo in constructing dwellings and ramadas. A ceiling of arrowweeds is strong enough to support a layer of mud that will keep rain out, but a thatch of pure *cachanilla* will do nearly as well. Young stalks can be woven to make large, strong baskets, cages, and nearly any sort of fixture for a house.

Arrowweed has medicinal uses as well, especially the roots. A poultice applied to a nervous or distraught child was thought to have a calming effect, and a tea was often used to temper digestive distress. There are also reports that the roots were used to produce a dye.

FAMILY	Asteraceae
OTHER NAMES	*cachanilla*
RANGE	throughout the Southwest
USES	tools, building, fiber, medicine, dye

4 · Barrel Cactus
Ferocactus spp.

There are several species of barrel cactus in the Southwest, each with different characteristics. They grow quite slowly. *F. wislizeni* tends to lean toward the south. Plants more than a yard tall may be nearly one hundred years old.

Many stories from early non-Indian desert travelers assured readers that barrel cacti could be tapped as a source of emergency water for those stranded in the desert. While the cacti do indeed harbor large quantities of water, getting at that water is a difficult task. The early observers made it sound as though lopping off the top and exposing the saturated pulp was a simple matter. In reality, barrels have a tough skin shielded by a network of ferocious, wire-tough spines often shaped like small daggers, straight or curved. This armament makes exposing the interior nearly impossible without a machete or axe. The marginally drinkable liquid is rather bitter, and the effort one must expend in extracting the liquid makes one thirsty, so the overall gain may be negligible.

Bruce Griffin

The fruits of *Ferocactus* are edible, though somewhat tart. There can be no harm in tasting them, for all fleshy cactus fruits are edible. The seeds, however, are far more accessible and are quite palatable, if somewhat tough. The fruits grow at the tip of the cactus and act as convenient capsules for the seeds. Twisting the ripe yellow fruits from the plant usually opens a small hole from which the seeds can easily be poured out like pills from a pill bottle and eaten raw. Many peoples parched the seeds of *Ferocactus* and ground them into tortillas, which they commonly ate when their supplies of corn ran out. Tortillas made from corn were considered by some to be inferior to tortillas made from barrel cactus seeds. The buds and flowers were a food source to people as well.

FAMILY	Cactaceae
OTHER NAMES	*biznaga*
RANGE	throughout the Southwest
USES	food, emergency water

5 · Beargrass
Nolina microcarpa

Rick and Nora Bowers

A close relative of sotol, beargrass (called *sacahuiste* in Mexico) has a flowering stalk with a showy panicle of flowers. The plants grow mostly above about 3,000 feet in elevation, often appearing in southwestern grasslands in the company of oaks and junipers.

As is the case with many relatives of the lily that bear flowering stalks, young beargrass stalks are edible when roasted. The buds and flowers are also edible, and some peoples found the roasted seeds to their liking.

Peoples of the Southwest wove baskets, mats, and sandals from the leaves and used them for thatching on huts. The leaves are an important part of Tohono O'odham basket making. The plant is rather scarce in the O'odham homelands, and women must travel to higher elevations to gather sheaves of the leaves to weave. This is not a project for the unskilled, for the margins of the leaf blades are nearly razor sharp. Many are the unfortunate souls who while climbing a hillside reached out and grabbed a handhold of beargrass leaves only to find their hand slashed and bloodied by the sharp, tearing edges.

FAMILY	Nolinaceae
OTHER NAMES	*sacahuiste*
RANGE	Arizona, New Mexico, Utah, northern Mexico
USES	food, fiber, baskets

6 · Big Sagebrush
Artemisia tridentata

FAMILY	Asteraceae
OTHER NAMES	*chamizo*
RANGE	throughout the Southwest
USES	fiber, wood, medicine, dye

These tough plants paint the landscape a smoky gray throughout much of the greater Southwest. Travelers passing through the Great Basin Desert of Nevada and Utah encounter vast landscapes in which big sagebrush is the dominant plant. They range in height from 2 to 7 feet, growing in what often appear to be pure stands. The plants tolerate aridity and cold, but not prolonged high temperatures. Antelope, deer, and goats thrive on the plant's leaves, but cattle do poorly. Local people easily recognize the smell of sagebrush after a rain, an aroma produced by the abundance of chemicals in the leaves.

As the most common plant of the interior western United States, big sagebrush presented many uses to native peoples. The bark hangs in shreds from the trunks and is easily harvested and separated into strips amenable to being woven or twisted into cord. Indigenous peoples fashioned numerous garments from the bark, including sandals, skirts, and shirts. It is readily flammable and thus ideal for tinder. The wood from the trunks makes good, aromatic firewood.

Although big sagebrush is not a major source of food, the leaves are rich in vitamins and minerals and when nibbled may constitute a good daily nutritional supplement. In larger amounts they may become toxic. Native peoples used the leaves to cure a variety of ailments, such as colds, headaches, rheumatism, and digestive disorders (including intestinal parasites). A tea brewed from the leaves may act as a stimulant. When boiled, the leaves and twigs also yield a yellow-gold dye.

Scott T. Smith

7 · Canegrass
Phragmites australis/Arundo donax

Throughout the Southwest, canegrass grows only in the presence of standing water or at least permanently moist soil. *Phragmites*, the original reed of the Southwest, is now uncommon, having been pushed aside by an aggressive European counterpart, *Arundo donax*. The two are so similar that only an expert can distinguish them.

Wendy Hodgson

For peoples of the Colorado and lower Gila rivers and of northwestern Mexico, the grass was indispensable and its uses were numerous and extraordinary. It was the material for weaving baskets and mats, and for building walls and roofs. The young shoots are tasty, and many peoples found them an important food source. Along the Colorado River huge numbers of aphids find the nodes of the cane attractive and deposit their honeydew on them, a sweet that peoples of the region considered a treat and collected. The roots, brewed into a tea, are still considered a sure remedy for various ailments. The dried, hollow canes, or poles, were a replacement for lumber, while lopped-off sections made for handy storage containers and musical instruments. A section with a node at one end and an open top at the other could be plugged with a simple cork to produce a portable container that could carry liquids or solids without danger of spillage. Musical flutes crafted from sections of *carrizo*, the Spanish name for canegrass, are still part of fiestas among native peoples of the region.

Dense thickets of *carrizo* form excellent wildlife habitat, offering food, protection, and concealment for a host of animals. The plants are responsive to even the slightest wind, whispering in a most agreeable hushed tone.

FAMILY	Poaceae
OTHER NAMES	*carrizo*, reed
RANGE	throughout the Southwest
USES	food, fiber, building, music, ceremony

8 · Canyon Grape
Vitis arizonica

Along southwestern perennial streams supporting diverse vegetation, I have occasionally found wild grapevines climbing high into the trees. With ample water, the plants will extend their tendrils and gradually blanket shrubs and even trees. They are more common in canyons of the sky island foothills, but sometimes find habitats with ashes, sycamores, and walnuts to their liking and bless the area with their fruits. The berries are much smaller than domesticated grapes, more the size of a pea. They are seldom as sweet as cultivated varieties, but they make superb jelly. When they ripen in the autumn, the collector must act quickly, since many other creatures find grapes enticing as well. I have seldom found enough grapes left on the vines to provide more than a nibble. When gathering grapes higher up in the mountains it is prudent to be on the lookout for bears seeking to fatten up on the succulent berries before heading for their sleeping quarters for the winter. Such bears may be grouchy with competitors. The vines may also share their habitat with poison ivy (*Rhus radicans*, Anacardiaceae), a three-leafed companion to grapevines that may turn a pleasant day of gathering into itching agony.

Wild grapes of different species are found in canyons throughout the Southwest. In some areas the vines spread out over large areas and produce enough grapes for a large harvest. Native peoples gathered them for making wine. Some dried them and preserved them for later consumption.

FAMILY	Vitaceae
OTHER NAMES	Arizona grape, *uva silvestre*
RANGE	Arizona, New Mexico, Nevada, Texas, Utah, northern Mexico
USES	food

9 · Canyon Ragweed
Ambrosia ambrosioides

Debra Valov

If you happen upon this common shrubby plant, it will be in a place subject to periodic flooding from summer rains. It grows only in washes and along southwestern watercourses and roadsides, and needs regular flooding to survive. The plants can tolerate serious floods, bending over parallel to the stream flow and then bouncing back to the upright position once the torrent has passed. They may reach 10 feet in height, with resilient stems and roots and large, wavy, dark green, triangular leaves.

Chicura, its name in Spanish, is one tough ragweed. It can be a downright ugly plant and the pollen brings misery to many allergy sufferers. Cattle avoid it, even during times of drought, and horses will not look twice at it. Oddly enough, though, burros and mules do not hesitate to grab a mouthful of the coarse, resinous leaves and seem to derive some nutrition from them. In rural Sonora when a young unmarried woman turns up pregnant, a common saying pronounces her and her lover to have been married "by Father Chicura in the Church of the Desert."

The leaves and stems of the plant are brewed into a tea widely administered to women following childbirth to prevent complications and speed healing. Native curers also believe the tea helps postpartum women regain their normal weight and figure. The same tea is also administered to women suffering from menstrual cramps. A diaper formed from a pad of leaves may alleviate urinary tract problems. And we thought ragweed was useless!

FAMILY	Asteraceae
OTHER NAMES	*chicura*
RANGE	Arizona, California, northern Mexico
USES	medicine

10 · Chiltepín
Capsicum annuum

FAMILY	Solanaceae
OTHER NAMES	wild chile
RANGE	Arizona, New Mexico, northern Mexico
USES	food

Chiltepín is the wild ancestor of many domesticated chiles. It grows in only a few places in the Southwest. In Sonora, Mexico, it is abundant in shady places in canyons and on moist slopes. The plants reach up to 6 feet in height, with small, white flowers that develop into chiles smaller than a pea.

Chiltepines are edible (with caution) as soon as they begin to resemble a chile pepper. When green, they have a fresh taste that is quickly overwhelmed by the heat of the capsaicin they contain. If the peppers are left to mature on the plants they turn red and become wildly popular with birds, which seem unaffected by the powerful burn the fruits produce in humans. In the sierras of eastern Sonora most families keep a plate of chiltepines on the table at all times. For decades, Tohono O'odham have gathered the fruits and marketed them, often marinated in vinegar, which makes for a most potent, if agreeable, condiment. Wild chiltepines are harvested by the ton in parts of Sonora, especially along the Río Sonora. In a few places attempts at domesticating the plants are under way. Just two or three of the dried fruits crumpled into a cup of salsa adds a powerful bite. Powdered chiltepín strategically placed can be an effective deterrent to unwanted visitors of any sort.

David Yetman

11 · Cholla
Cylindropuntia spp.

The genus *Cylindropuntia* includes at least a dozen species. Ranchers and hikers learn quickly about these plants, especially the jumping cholla *(C. bigelovii)*, which has spiny joints so delicately attached to the plant that a slight brush will attach them to a passerby. The Tohono O'odham and Akimel O'odham still consider the buds of the buckhorn cholla *(C. acanthocarpa)* as a basic food, perhaps their most important wild vegetable. In spite of their fresh appearance, the buds usually sport ample spines and *glochids*—tiny hairlike bristles that appear soft and nonthreatening but are really barbed and painful and attach to skin by the dozen. The spines and glochids must be removed before one attempts to eat the fruits. A mouthful of cholla spines is nothing to envy and glochids are very tricky to extract. The best way to remove them is by rolling the buds around with a stiff brush, or rubbing them by hand after they have been roasted. Native peoples harvested the buds, which when cooked have a delicate flavor. They also ground cooked, dried buds with other native seeds to make *atole*, or thin porridge.

Rick and Nora Bowers

The Seri of northwestern Mexico harvest the fruits of the chainfruit cholla (*C. fulgida*) as well, brushing the fruits with shrub branches to remove the glochids. Others hold the individual fruits with any instrument at all and lop off the husk, leaving the juicy pulp. It is piquant, but the Seri learned long ago that adding a couple of drops of lime juice tempers the acidity and makes them tasty, though still sour.

A variety of cholla species also grows at higher elevations throughout the Southwest, and the seeds, buds, and fruits provided a source of food for Puebloans and the Southern Paiute as well.

FAMILY	Cactaceae
OTHER NAMES	*choya*
RANGE	throughout the Southwest
USES	food

12 · Cottonwood
Populus fremontii

Larry Ulrich

Cottonwoods line streams throughout the desert Southwest, often reaching heights of more than 100 feet, creating ribbons of green in an otherwise parched landscape. Over the last century their numbers have become much reduced due to widespread lowering of water tables, while commercial and industrial water interests have been responsible for the felling of countless trees as a water-salvage strategy.

Cottonwood is so named because of the clouds of wispy seeds that seem to flow from the branches in the spring. Winds can transport them for miles. They can make a mess after a couple of days as they lodge in every accessible crevice.

The beauty of these large-leafed trees and the shade they provide have been a comfort as long as humans have populated the Southwest. In addition, the wood (though soft and not especially durable) has long been valued for its workability and texture, even sufficing as beams for houses. It is most amenable to being worked into masks and cylinders for drums, and the dried-out roots of dead trees are widely used by the Hopi for carving kachinas. Strips of cottonwood branches and bark can be woven into baskets. The bark has purported curative powers, and many peoples use it for binding and treating bruises, sprains, strains, and even broken bones. The catkins (the tree's buds) and flowers are edible.

FAMILY	Salicaceae
OTHER NAMES	*álamo*
RANGE	throughout the Southwest
USES	building, ceremony, music, food, medicine, tools, baskets

13 · Creosote
Larrea divaricata

This tough shrub is one of the most common plants of the desert portions of the Southwest. It typically grows to 4 to 6 feet in height, but may reach 20 feet. In some landscapes creosotes appear to be the only shrub growing. Creosote is adept at extracting the last traces of water from the soil. The plants can be very resinous, which is part of their water-conservation strategy. The smallish flowers are bright yellow, and in wet years they contrast with the dark green of the leaves. Some creosotes may be more than 12,000 years old, making them the world's oldest plants.

Creosote has survived over millions of acres of desert due in part to the wealth of chemicals its leaves and stems manufacture both to deter herbivores and to prevent water loss. They produce a characteristic odor and for many southwesterners the smell of the desert after the first summer rain is a fond memory. The same scent rises from the small, furry fruits and the leaves when crushed between the fingers.

The healing properties of creosote are known far beyond its habitat. Leaves and branches brewed into a tea are thought by many herbalists to be "good for what ails you"—colds, sore throats, rheumatism, bad liver, and fever. The Seri consider a very hot decoction of the leaves and stems applied to a stingray jab as the best remedy. Two women treated such a wound in my son in the late 1960s as he writhed in pain after an encounter with a stingray. As soon as they began to apply the hot liquid, the excruciating pain subsided. The wound healed perfectly.

A handful of creosote branches used as a brush can sweep away glochids from prickly pear fruits. A scale insect on the branches secretes a resin that many peoples use as an all-purpose adhesive and filler.

Rick and Nora Bowers

FAMILY	Zygophyllaceae
OTHER NAMES	*gobernadora, hediondilla*
RANGE	throughout the Southwest
USES	medicine, tools

14 · Crucillo
Condalia warnockii

FAMILY	Rhamnaceae
OTHER NAMES	snakewood
RANGE	Arizona, New Mexico, Texas, northern Mexico
USES	food, wood

Crucillos are smallish shrubs, rarely reaching 5 feet in height, with dense, dark green leaves and numerous thorny branches. They grow mostly in upland portions of the Sonoran Desert. The thorns and branches are less offensive than they seem, more inclined to scratch than to pierce the skin.

These plants would be entirely unremarkable were it not for their edible, pea-sized berries, black to reddish-black in color. They are sweet, but harbor a large seed that occupies most of the fruit. They are reminiscent of hackberries (*Celtis* spp.) in that one must expend considerable energy in order to achieve a caloric gain. The thorns may harbor a mild poison that makes punctures painful.

The wood is nearly as hard and tough as that of mesquite, providing excellent firewood. Some prehistoric peoples may have planted the bushes in the vicinity of their homes.

Bruce Griffin

15 · Datura
Datura discolor, annual
Datura wrightii, perennial

FAMILY	Solanaceae
OTHER NAMES	jimsonweed, *toloache,* thorn apple, moonflower
RANGE	throughout the Southwest
USES	medicine, ceremony

Do *not* eat any part of these plants or drink liquids derived from them. All of datura's parts—roots, stems, leaves, seeds, flowers, and fruits—are laden with powerful chemicals that produce disastrous, mind-altering, and sometimes deadly effects on the central nervous system. They grow throughout much of the Southwest.

Datura is one of our most noticeable and attractive plants, with spreading, dark or bright green leaves and huge, inviting, white to purplish flowers that are pollinated by sphinx moths. The fruits are diabolical appearing structures, resembling Ping-Pong balls with numerous mean-looking spines. Datura often appears growing by itself, springing as if by magic from barren, disturbed soils—especially in places like livestock corrals and water tanks, where it thrives. Livestock will not touch the plant, or even trample it, which is a good reason for us to avoid it as well.

Still, some native curers believe the alkaloids contained in the leaves make them medicinally powerful. Some report that the leaves can be heated on a stove and applied directly to wounds, bruises, sprains, broken bones, or inflammations (including hemorrhoids) while taking all precautions to avoid any contact with open sores that might absorb some of the potent alkaloids that abound in the plant. Admiring the plant's beauty, while not touching any part of it, is a prudent policy.

Rick and Nora Bowers

16 · Deerweed
Porophyllum gracile

Deerweed, or *odorato*, is a common, small, inconspicuous plant that prefers rocky substrates throughout the arid Southwest. Neither it nor its white or purplish flowers are especially distinctive, and in dry times the plant may shrivel up completely. However, the plant gives off the sort of smell people find either attractive or repulsive. *P. gracile* grows quickly after rains, becoming succulent. The human nose can detect the plants at some distance, well before the plant is spotted, due to powerful and volatile oils and terpenes given off from the leaves. In Arizona the plants seldom grow more than a foot or so tall. Farther south in Mexico they may reach 3 feet in height. When the leaves and stems are crushed between the fingers, the scent permeates the skin, often beyond the power of soap to remove. Several native peoples imbue it with remarkable powers of healing and curing. A tea brewed from the pungent leaves may alleviate menstrual cramps and assist women who wish to become pregnant. The tea is also a popular remedy to relieve muscle cramps.

C. Allan Morgan

FAMILY	Asteraceae
OTHER NAMES	slender poreleaf, *odorato, hierba de venado*
RANGE	sporadic throughout the Southwest
USES	medicine

17 · Desert Fan Palm
Washingtonia filifera

One of nature's ironies is the range of the desert fan palm—it grows almost exclusively in the hottest, driest parts of American deserts. It is abundant in oases of the southern California desert, especially in canyons of the San Jacinto Mountains, but grows in only two locations in Arizona. The trees can survive only where their roots have permanent access to water. Several groves sprout incongruously from the trace of the San Andreas Fault in the Coachella Valley, where the action of the plates grinding laterally against each other has produced sediments so fine that they block the flow of underground water into the valley from mountains to the north. The water finds its way nearly to the surface, providing just the moisture the palms need.

Larry Ulrich

The desert fan palm was of incalculable importance to Native Americans for shade, food, and construction materials. Palm fruits, though small, resemble dates in their flavor, sweetness, nutrients, and abundance. When dried they can be ground, seeds and all, into a flour and stored. The leaves are a fine source of fiber for making baskets, cords, sandals, and coarse textiles. They can be interwoven into a thatched roof that sheds water and maintains an interior domestic temperature that is cool in summer and warm in winter. The wood can be used to make furnishings light in weight but strong. Shade in a palm oasis may remain as much as 25 degrees cooler than the surrounding exposed country during the hot summer months.

Native Americans discovered hundreds of years ago that periodic burning of the dried fronds spurs the palms to new growth and kills off potential pests and competitors. The burning in no way harms the trees, whose trunks are nearly pure water.

FAMILY	Arecaceae
OTHER NAMES	California fan palm, *palma*
RANGE	Arizona, California, Nevada, northern Mexico
USES	food, fiber, building

18 · Desert Lavender
Hyptis emoryi

Debra Valov

This plant is well named, for its small lavender blossoms give off a delicate and pleasing fragrance like that of no other plant. It prefers disturbed soils along dry washes and seems to tolerate droughts rather well. The tall, straight stalks that grow to more than 10 feet in height will bow to ephemeral flooding, then return to their upright position. In the torturous lava flows of Mexico's Pinacate volcanic field, it is one of the early and successful plants to emerge from the relatively young lava.

Desert lavender's agreeable aroma, and seeds that expand when moistened, give it a multitude of uses. Sprigs of the blossoms improve the atmosphere in any house. The smoke is sweet-smelling and purifying. Burning a few stalks in an enclosed room will cleanse the area of foul odors and, some say, toxins. Taking in some of the seeds mixed with water may alleviate stomach distress and constipation. A tea from the leaves has calming powers, according to some. The seeds quickly absorb water, and some native curers use them to remove stubborn foreign objects from the eye, and to treat earache as well. Some old reports suggest that the stalks were used as arrows.

FAMILY	Lamiaceae
OTHER NAMES	*bíbino, salvia*
RANGE	Arizona, California, Nevada, northern Mexico
USES	home, medicine, tools

19 · Devil's Claw
Proboscidea spp.

FAMILY	Martyniaceae
OTHER NAMES	*aguaro,* doubleclaw, unicorn plant
RANGE	throughout the Southwest
USES	food, fiber

Proboscideas are classically useful desert plants with fruits among the oddest in the world. *P. altheaefolia* is a perennial with a somewhat edible storage root, while the annual *P. parviflora* has only a tiny root. The plants shrivel after the rains and remain nearly hidden through the dry season.

The succulent, sticky-leafed plants of both species appear after summer rains commence and grow rapidly, especially in overgrazed areas with silty or sandy soils. The buds produce flowers that are showy yellow *(P. altheaefolia)* or pink *(P. parviflora)*. The fascinating part of the plant's growth begins when the flowers dry and the fruits—pods resembling okra—develop. Succulent at first, these dry toward the tip and begin to split in half. At this stage each side has an elongated tip that curls outward in the middle and inward and upward at the points, forming an ominous-looking claw about 6 inches long. When the fruits dry completely, the "claws" take on the resilience of coiled springs. Though the last vestiges of the original plants wilt, dry, and disappear, the claws often rest hidden among dead leaves and other plants and, when tread upon, they are poised to spring upward and grab the unaware passerby by the foot or ankle in what can be a momentarily terrifying experience. The claws, called *aguaro* in Mexico, are curiously attractive, and people often collect them as ornaments.

When the claws are pulled apart, the capsule—now dry and tough—splits and exposes the seeds. These are edible, though chewy and somewhat dry, with a flavor reminiscent of sunflower seeds.

Tohono O'odham basket makers use a strip of black fiber from the claws of *P. parviflora* as an integral part of their baskets. These splints provide the black-colored portion of the design that contrasts so agreeably with the white of the yucca fiber. O'odham people have semi-domesticated the long-clawed *P. parviflora* for its edible seeds and for the fiber to weave in their baskets.

Rick and Nora Bowers

20 · Elderberry
Sambucus nigra

Rick and Nora Bowers

One seldom sees these large shrubs or small trees any more in the Southwest. They live in moist places, especially along streams and washes, which in the United States have suffered greatly from the banes of cattle trampling and development. They are still common in Mexico just south of the border, where they form attractive hedgerows along highways and washes, and in other parts of the American West, blooming with sprays of pretty white blossoms in summertime. The fruits are bluish and usually tasty. Some people warn against eating them in excess, mentioning vague digestive problems that may ensue.

The fruits were formerly very popular with native peoples, who ate them right off the bush, or gathered, dried, and pressed them, and even made them into a sort of cake. The fruits evidently ferment rather well, producing a wine whose potency drew the wrath of Jesuit priests, both for the drunkenness it produced and for its lingering effects, which interfered with the natives' work ethic for several days. Some people still produce elderberry wine. Be careful.

Native peoples used the flowers and leaves to brew a tea that they drank as a remedy for various ailments. Extracts of the flowers and fruit are used today in over-the-counter pharmaceuticals that claim immune-boosting properties.

FAMILY	Caprifoliaceae
OTHER NAMES	*tápiro, sauco*
RANGE	throughout the Southwest
USES	food, medicine, beverage

21 · Fourwing Saltbush
Atriplex canescens

The humble saltbush is well named, as a nibble on a leaf will reveal. The plants are usually low lying, but under ideal conditions may reach more than 10 feet in height. They can tolerate severe drought. *A. canescens* is a rather nondescript species, yet it possesses two remarkable properties: it can tolerate salty or alkaline soils that are lethal to other species, and while plants are either male or female, they may change sex in response to drought. They also may take on rather different appearances and shades of gray or green, depending on the habitat in which they grow. They are common from the salty flats near the Gulf of California to the mesas of the Four Corners region and in arid soils throughout the western United States. In spite of the salty taste of the leaves, saltbush is popular with numerous birds and many browsers, including deer and bighorn sheep. Goats also find the leaves and seeds palatable. In a pinch, even we can eat the leaves.

Fourwing saltbush has an admirable diversity of uses. Branches, living or dead, make excellent, fast-burning fuel, a most useful property in drier deserts where fuelwood is often scarce. The ashes are rich in salt: some native peoples add them to blue cornmeal, either to alter its flavor or to preserve its natural color when cooked. The seeds, which grow by fours in membranous capsules, are edible, though much labor must be expended to gather them.

The leaves and roots appear in native medicine throughout the Southwest. Parts of the plant are used for stomach pain; as a purgative; and for infections, insect bites, and toothache. Some also use the ashes for a hair tonic.

The leaves when boiled yield a yellow dye. The branches are bushy enough to provide improvised emergency shelter.

Bruce Griffin

FAMILY	Chenopodiaceae
OTHER NAMES	*chamizo cenizo*
RANGE	throughout the Southwest
USES	dye, food, tools, medicine

22 · Graythorn
Ziziphus obtusifolia

FAMILY	Rhamnaceae
OTHER NAMES	lotebush, *jutuqui*
RANGE	throughout the Southwest
USES	food, medicine, soap

Rick and Nora Bowers

Graythorn is a rather unattractive bush that spends much of the year without leaves, which are sparse and small anyway. The branches are numerous, grayish or sometimes slightly green, and terminate with a sharp tip. In the vegetation alongside arroyos or desert washes, it may form thickets that slow anyone trying to pass. The bushes flower opportunistically following rains with tiny, white, inconspicuous blossoms. The plants are common throughout the desert habitats of the Southwest.

In spite of its drab, unfriendly appearance, graythorn enjoys a good reputation among native peoples. Its fruits, the size and color of blueberries, are edible—though not especially tasty. In their habitat they are an important food source for birds as well as people.

The roots and branches are widely used for healing. Soap can be produced from pounded roots. A powder from the same roots, or a tea from the branches, is applied to sores of various kinds, especially those that will not heal. The tea is a remedy for syphilis, cancer, and digestive distress. It is also administered to stroke victims to help them regain use of their normal faculties.

23 · Hackberry
Celtis pallida, Celtis reticulata

FAMILY	Ulmaceae
OTHER NAMES	*cúmero, cumbro*
RANGE	Arizona, New Mexico, Texas, northern Mexico
USES	food

The hackberry is a relative of the elm tree. Throughout the Southwest, hackberries grow as shrubs *(C. pallida)* on hillsides and above watercourses where they form thickets, and as trees *(C. reticulata)* growing in bottomlands where they may reach 30 feet in height. The branches sport long thorns that turn out not to be as intimidating as they appear. The bright orange berries (the size of a pea) of these evergreen plants are sweet, though sometimes dry. They contain seeds that make up most of the fruit. Even so, they make for a tasty snack, but probably require more calories for the labor of harvesting than they provide when eaten. Gathering enough for a mouthful presents a challenge to the hungry hiker. During rainy years the berries become juicier and seem to encourage ingestion. They provide an important food source for a variety of birds and desert mammals.

24 · Hedgehog Cactus
Echinocereus spp.

FAMILY	Cactaceae
OTHER NAMES	*pitayita*
RANGE	throughout the Southwest
USES	food

This is an oddly named cactus, since it has no obvious resemblance to a hedgehog other than its spiny presentation. The cactus consists of multiple stems, usually of different heights, mostly less than 1 foot tall. As forbidding as the plants may appear from their host of menacing spines, their flowers (magenta in color) are among the showiest in the Southwest. Even better, this cactus yields some of the sweetest fruits of any desert plant, collected and eaten by many native peoples throughout the Southwest. Though the fruits are covered with mean spines as they develop, they shed the spines when they ripen and seem to invite the gatherer to partake of the pinkish pulp laced with tiny black seeds. One cannot be casual about gathering them, however, since a host of creatures—including insects, birds, and mammals—finds them as tasty as we do and usually beats the human collector to the punch. The fruits usually ripen in May and June, well before the saguaro fruits become available, and thus provide a tantalizing appetizer to the more prominent saguaro fruit harvest.

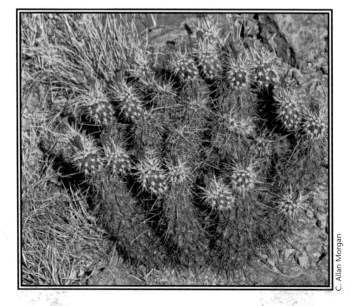

C. Allan Morgan

Olneya tesota

Bruce Griffin

The venerable ironwood grows only in warmer portions of the Southwest. Given its sensitivity to freezing, over the centuries it gained a reputation as a good indicator of places where citrus trees will thrive. It also tolerates drought and high temperatures as well as any other desert tree. The trees live to a great age, perhaps as much as 900 years, often developing massive trunks. Following death, their trunks resist rot and may survive above the ground for 1,000 years. Collecting of the wood has vastly depleted the stock of dead trunks, however. In northern Mexico the charcoal industry has decimated the oldest living trees.

Ironwood flowers in late spring, and in those years when the trees choose to bloom in profusion, their delicate pink and fragrant blossoms enhance the landscape. Some years the trees may bloom little or not at all. The tiny leaves fall to the ground and produce a most fertile litter—a mulch that combines with the nitrogen-producing nodules on ironwood's roots to nourish literally hundreds of other plants.

Ironwood is the densest and hardest wood of the desert regions. While it resists carving, it can be chipped and sanded into fine sculptures, an art that the Seri developed in the 1960s. The wood is also excellent firewood, but it burns so hot that one must be experienced with its nature to avoid burning food and damaging cookware.

The seeds may taste bitter when removed from the pod, but many native peoples discovered long ago that soaking them in water or parching them removed the bitterness, thus making them palatable and even tasty. Whoever discovered the method of preparation deserves the gratitude of many people, for the seeds became an important food source for many desert dwellers.

FAMILY	Fabaceae
OTHER NAMES	*palo fierro*
RANGE	Arizona, California, northern Mexico
USES	food, wood

26 · Jojoba
Simmondsia chinensis

FAMILY	Simmondsiaceae
OTHER NAMES	goatnut
RANGE	Arizona, California, northern Mexico
USES	food, oil

The jojoba prefers those areas of the Southwest that are hot but not too hot, not too wet, and not too dry. The shrubby, handsome plants have an agreeable size, reaching 10 feet in height and an equal breadth. The abundant, leathery leaves, of a gray-green color, seem perfectly adapted to withstand extended drought.

Jojobas are dioecious, meaning that plants may bear male or female flowers. Only the females produce fruits. These are nutlike, the size of a small acorn, with kernels resembling large pine nuts. People have varying opinions about jojoba's culinary virtue. Some find the nuts tasty and edible; others pronounce them bitter and unpalatable. Still others find them inedible, producing digestive malfunctions. Some native peoples prepare them into edible foods using a variety of techniques including roasting the fruits, then grinding the toasted remnants for a coffee-type drink. Others avoid consuming them altogether. Some use the oil as a shampoo, a point not lost on marketers of high-end cosmetics.

Jojoba fruits are 50 percent oil in the form of an oily wax. The oil is indigestible but of extremely high quality for industrial purposes. It matches sperm whale oil in purity and viscosity, all the better for the whale, which is now protected. Various projects in the Southwest and elsewhere in the world's deserts have involved cultivation of jojoba on a commercial scale in hopes of marketing the oil.

While humans find the nuts useful and even nutritious, animals, except perhaps for goats, do not gobble them as they might cactus fruits. It is as though they understand that these are a natural product to be taken only in moderation, if at all.

C. Allan Morgan

27 · Juniper
Juniperus spp.

FAMILY	Cupressaceae
OTHER NAMES	*táscate*
RANGE	throughout the Southwest
USES	food, medicine, fiber, building

The most notable change in vegetation in the Southwest as one gains elevation from the desert into the mountains is the appearance of junipers. Their dark, round shape appears unmistakably on hillsides and flats at somewhat over 3,000 feet elevation. *J. monosperma* is common throughout the Southwest, while *J. osteosperma*, the Utah juniper, is common north of the Gila River into the Colorado Plateau. Junipers tolerate extended drought and great heat.

The fruits—in reality small cones—are marginally edible though rather unpalatable, better used for flavoring than as a basic food. During hard times, native peoples derived some nutrition from these tough "berries," but only with considerable expenditure of labor. Many critters seem to gnaw on them. In Europe they constituted the flavoring for gin.

Juniper wood heats thousands of homes in the Southwest. It not only burns slowly and leaves little ash, but its smoke is fragrant and inoffensive. The bark is soft and stringy and can easily be removed without damaging the tree. It is useful as tinder for starting fires. Its springy texture makes it useful for stuffing bedding and as diaper padding for generations of southwestern babies. It can be twisted into cord as well. The trunks make strong and long-lasting fence posts, perhaps to the trees' detriment. Some junipers grow large enough to provide shade and comfort. The bark, cambium, and fruits have a variety of medicinal uses as well.

Bruce Griffin

28 · Mesquite
Prosopis spp.

Mesquites are all-purpose plants of the Southwest. They yield food, firewood, lumber, medicine, and shade. The three species have somewhat different characteristics, but all were important for indigenous people as producers of edible beans.

C. Allan Morgan

The pods, which appear from late May through June (and sometimes in October as well) have sustained native peoples for thousands of years. Called *péchitas* in Mexico, they constituted the basic starch in the diet of many southwestern peoples, and they were prepared in a variety of ways. Some native peoples staked out ownership of individual trees or of collecting areas, an indication of how vitally important the pods were.

The golden-colored sap hardens into a semi-malleable mass with a sweet flavor, tastier in some locations than in others. It becomes a natural candy, a fine adhesive, a filler, a remedy for colds and flu, and an all-purpose resin.

C. Allan Morgan

Mesquite blossoms are the source of some of the world's finest honey. The flowers themselves are edible, with a sweet flavor, though one must heed the many insects that forage among them as well.

Various parts of the mesquite have medicinal uses. The roots, bark, sap, and leaves all play roles in traditional southwestern medicine, curing such maladies as conjunctivitis, intestinal parasites, acne, and dandruff.

Many people consider mesquite charcoal to be the best for grilling meats, although charcoal manufacture has resulted in the felling of many thousands of grand trees hundreds of years old. As a result, most of the great patriarch mesquites have been sacrificed to grill meats. For houses and furniture, the wood is unsurpassed.

FAMILY	Fabaceae
OTHER NAMES	*mezquite*
RANGE	throughout the southwestern deserts
USES	food, medicine, wood

29 · Mormon Tea
Ephedra spp.

Tom Bean

People are often surprised to learn that ephedra is a gymnosperm—a member of the conifer order—more closely related to pines and firs than to flowering plants. A close examination of the fruits quickly shows them to be cones and their classification is instantly justified. The genus is widespread, though in the American West it appears to be quite well adapted to arid landscapes and one is seldom far from an ephedra plant. These three species, *E. aspera*, *E. californica*, and *E. trifurca*, frequent different habitats but are quite similar in appearance.

Some of the world's sixty species of ephedra contain ephedrine, a stimulant and decongestant often effective in countering the symptoms of the common cold. Early settlers in the Southwest believed that our ephedras contained a mild stimulant that could be activated by chewing or sucking on the stems or brewing them into a tea. Others believed the stems contained chemicals effective against a wide variety of infirmities, including syphilis. Native peoples used the stems and roots for medicine to treat many ailments. Navajos used the twigs to dye wool as well.

Whether or not our ephedras contain stimulants is hard to say, but I have always found that chomping on a couple of stems is pleasant. The juice from the stems has a tendency to dry out the mouth, so be sure to carry water if you plan to chew away.

FAMILY	Ephedraceae
OTHER NAMES	joint-fir, *cañutillo, tepopote*
RANGE	throughout the Southwest
USES	stimulant, medicine, dye

30 · Mountain Mahogany
Cercocarpus montanus

Although mountain mahogany grows most profusely in piñon-juniper vegetation, it is tough enough to survive at the upper edges of the desert, where it is a resilient shrub. At higher elevations it may grow into a tree. Its most distinctive feature is the silvery plume that extends a few inches from the tip of the fruits and usually persists for several months. Native Americans long ago noticed that its leaves, though sparse, were popular with deer, which rely on the plant for browse.

Indigenous people also recognized many centuries ago that mountain mahogany is among the strongest, hardest, and handsomest woods of the Southwest, stronger than and nearly as hard as ironwood. Hispanics call the plant *palo duro,* "tough wood," with good reason. The wood resembles mahogany and is as pretty as it is durable. Long before the arrival of Europeans, people were fashioning it into tools of all shapes and sizes—planting sticks, bows, tool handles, loom parts, and even clubs.

The bark of mountain mahogany is nearly as useful as the wood. When boiled in water it produces a russet-colored pigment ideal for dyeing. The color varies when combined with other plants or materials, making it the basis for a wide range of hues. The bark also has medicinal qualities, especially when brewed into a tea. New Mexican Hispanics believed that sprinkling twigs around one's bed would ward off bedbugs.

Although it is classified as a member of the rose family, the roots of mountain mahogany can fix nitrogen and enrich the soil in their vicinity just as

many legumes do. It grows throughout the Southwest and extends east into the edge of the prairies.

J. S. Peterson, USDA-NRCS PLANTS Database

FAMILY	Rosaceae
OTHER NAMES	*palo duro*
RANGE	throughout the Southwest
USES	tools, dye, wood

31 · Oak
Quercus spp.

Many species of oak grow throughout the greater Southwest, dotting foothills and grasslands with enchanting green canopies. They are most common above 4,000 feet elevation.

The Emory oak *(Q. emoryi)* is the Southwest's handsomest and largest, and produces the most edible acorns. Trees reach nearly 50 feet in height and may grow even wider. *Bellotas,* as they are called in Spanish, usually grow in deep soils in association with rich forage grasses, combining to present one of the Southwest's fairest landscapes.

Rick and Nora Bowers

Oak leaves are dark green in color with an irregular margin. The acorns are usually sweet and tasty, although the quality varies from tree to tree. Acorns were especially popular with Apaches and other native peoples, who regularly collected them in early summer well into the latter part of the twentieth century. They ground the acorn kernels into meal and formed it into cakes. In Sonora, Mexico, vendors often hawk large bags of bellota acorns along the highways. Cowboys in the area have relied on them as trail food for centuries. Bears find the acorns particularly tasty and tend to frequent bellota country during acorn season. The wood is frequently the best firewood in its habitat and has been used for centuries for smoking meats. When freshly cut (especially when green), however, the wood often gives off the odor of vomit, strong enough to attract swarms of flies. Other oak species provide fine firewood as well.

Rick and Nora Bowers

Most oaks are populated with oak galls, cherry-sized growths that result from infestation by the larvae of certain wasps. While the galls are inedible, they are good sources of tannin for curing leather and dyeing weaving material. Native peoples have also pounded or ground the galls and applied the resulting astringent powder to burns, sores, and bruises.

FAMILY	Fagaceae
OTHER NAMES	*bellota, encino, roble*
RANGE	throughout the Southwest
USES	food, medicine, tannins, wood, dye

32 · Ocotillo
Fouquieria splendens

Rick and Nora Bowers

These sticklike plants, which reach 20 feet in height, are members of a strange and intriguing family that includes the exotic boojum tree of Baja California. Ocotillos resemble no other plants in the Western Hemisphere. In the Southwest they are common in the deserts adjacent to Mexico.

While the ocotillos (the family includes eleven species) all have stout spines, they are not cacti. They have a fondness for a variety of soils, especially limestone. During long droughts, the plants may seem to be dead. When rains do arrive, they leaf out almost overnight, quickly taking on a dark green, lush or velvety appearance. Not long after the branches leaf out, the plants flower, sending out from the branch tips bright red tubular inflorescences that appeal to birds, especially hummingbirds.

Indigenous peoples have found medicinal properties in the roots and bark.

Tohono O'odham carefully remove the buds and suck at the base of the flowers. The reward is a brief and tantalizing taste of sweetness. One can sample the flowers for hours without getting full.

Ocotillo branches make excellent fencing, especially useful since the cut branches tend to sprout and grow once they are placed in the ground. Desert peoples have also used them to build the basic structure for ramadas and huts. These may last only a season or two, but if the cut branches take root, they and their descendants will be there for years.

The word *ocotillo* is derived from the Aztec *ocote*, which means "torch." So an ocotillo is a little torch. When the fiery flowers are in full bloom the name makes sense.

Rick and Nora Bowers

FAMILY	Fouquieriaceae
OTHER NAMES	none
RANGE	throughout the southwestern deserts
USES	food, building

33 · Organ Pipe Cactus
Stenocereus thurberi

The organ pipe cactus is common in the warmer parts of the Sonoran Desert, where it is also known by the name *pitaya dulce*. It is abundant in Organ Pipe Cactus National Monument, which happens to be the most frost-free part of Arizona. A degree of freezing that saguaros can tolerate will kill organ pipes, hence their more restricted range. Though not as tall as the saguaro, they may reach 40 feet in height with hundreds of arms. They probably live to be at least 150 years old. Organ pipe branches are thinner than those of the saguaro and branch at the base, whereas saguaros branch well above the ground.

The fruits are covered with vicious spines, but when the ripe fruits are collected, the spines usually slough off in a few hours. The fruits thus gain protection from any creature that would harvest them before the seeds are ready to germinate.

Among indigenous people the organ pipe is best known for its fruits, which ripen in midsummer. The pulp is usually bright red in color and intensely sweet and juicy. For most native peoples of the area, the fruits formed an essential part of their diet. For the Tohono O'odham, the harvest of the fruits marked a festive time of year. In Mexico many people gather the fruits, called *pitayas,* and sell them in local markets. Some also produce jam and fruit leather from the pulp.

The wood from the branches is especially suited for making fences around houses, with closely placed stakes assuring privacy. The woody branches stripped of green matter make for excellent ceiling beams, as long as they are kept dry.

FAMILY	Cactaceae
OTHER NAMES	*pitaya dulce*
RANGE	Arizona, northern Mexico
USES	food, building

$\mathcal{34}$ · Paloverde
Parkinsonia spp.

FAMILY	Fabaceae
OTHER NAMES	none
RANGE	throughout the southwestern deserts
USES	food

Larry Ulrich

*P*alo verde in Spanish means "green pole," a reference to the green bark of paloverde trunks. This bark is physiologically active, enabling the trees to carry on photosynthesis whether they are leafless or in leaf.

Paloverdes are probably the most common trees in the Sonoran Desert. Blue paloverde *(P. florida)* and foothills paloverde (*P. microphylla*) grow abundantly in the Sonoran Desert. During the spring, the flowers of these paloverdes transform desert hillsides and valleys into a brilliant yellow tapestry. Both species are planted as ornamentals. Foothills paloverdes are very slow growers, but live for hundreds of years. They constitute the most important nurse plants for saguaros. Blue paloverdes grow more quickly and become taller, but have a far shorter life span.

The seeds of foothills paloverde constituted a basic food for many native peoples. Some folks also ate the seeds of blue paloverde, though they are less tasty. They devised a variety of methods for removing the pods, usually toasting them (to make them more palatable and to kill insect larvae), then grinding the seeds, and then adding water to the resultant flour to make *pinole,* a thick porridge, or *atole,* a drinkable porridge. They sometimes mixed the flour with that of other legumes. Some peoples warned against eating the seeds raw.

35 · Peppergrass
Lepidium spp.

FAMILY	Brassicaceae
OTHER NAMES	pepperweed, *mostaza*
RANGE	throughout the Southwest
USES	food

One can easily overlook peppergrass, since most species are low-lying annuals dependent on winter rains. If these rains fail, as they often do, the annuals will be absent. On those happy years with adequate *equipatas*, as winter rains are known in northern Mexico, peppergrass grows abundantly on disturbed soils, its delicate white flowers contrasting with the green leaves. The greens are edible, but it is the green seeds that have the delightful, strong flavor of mustard and pepper that warms the mouth and clears the nasal passages. It is a tasty mustard-like addition to salads as well. Gathering sufficient greens and seeds for a salad may take quite some time, however, since the plants seldom grow in pure stands. Once the plants dry out, the seeds become tough and tasteless.

The spicy seeds of peppergrass are rich in mucilage, which is an excellent source of fiber in the diet and may play an important role in controlling diabetes. One would have to gather quite a number of seeds to benefit from this property, but gathering is fun and the rewards are good taste and, perhaps, better health.

C. Allan Morgan

36 · Piñon
Pinus edulis (Colorado piñon)
P. monophylla (single-leaf piñon)

C. Allan Morgan

The piñon pine, the state tree of New Mexico, grows throughout the Southwest and although not usually thought of as a desert tree, it can survive under nearly desert conditions. In the Southwest piñons may grow as low as 4,000 feet and tolerate blistering heat and drought. They grow in southwestern mountains and frequently intermingle with junipers. The trees are usually small, seldom exceeding 40 feet in height.

Piñons made life better for native peoples, providing them with food, resin, and firewood. Pine nuts are a staple food for many indigenous people and a healthful snack for many others, and are also the basis for pesto. The nuts, or seeds, are rich in oil and protein and have a delicate, sweet flavor. They grow embedded within the piñon cones and require a little practice to extract. When they ripen, all manner of creatures race to see who can gather the most.

Piñon pines and their cones teem with resin, part of the plant's protection against insect borers, which are rapidly drowned in the gooey sap, and against drying out in the prolonged dry spells common in the region. Nut gatherers must be prepared to return home with patches of the pitch adhering to their skin and clothing.

The wood makes good, though fast-burning, firewood. Gathering, cutting, and handling the wood is sure to produce contact with the resin, so care must be taken. The pitch is easily removed from skin by rubbing the site of contact with dirt and can also be removed if necessary with a solvent. All of these characteristics made the resin ideal for waterproofing baskets and jugs, for gluing items together, and for filling unwanted crevices. It also makes a fine incense.

FAMILY	Pinaceae
OTHER NAMES	pinyon, *piñón*
RANGE	throughout the Southwest
USES	food, resin, wood

What many people pass over as a common weed plays an important role in nutrition and digestion. Plantains, like peppergrass, are somewhat unusual in that they grow in response to winter, not summer, rains. These plants, with easily plucked seed heads that turn velvety in maturity, grow in great numbers throughout the Southwest and elsewhere in the world.

The dry seeds detach from the stems without great difficulty. When they are immersed in water, they swell rapidly and become gummy or slimy from the mucilage they exude, similar to the action of desert lavender *(Hyptis emoryi)* and peppergrass *(Lepidium* spp.). Thus, they serve as food and provide bulk to the digestive system. Psyllium seed, a popular remedy for constipation and diarrhea, is a closely related species of *Plantago.*

Indigenous peoples routinely gathered the seeds and made them into a refreshing drink—quite tasty, though the slimy aspect of the mucilage can be disconcerting to the uninitiated. Some evidence suggests that the mucilaginous seeds produce a bulking effect in the human gut that may retard digestion of sugars and play a role in fending off diabetes.

Debra Valov

FAMILY	Plantaginaceae
OTHER NAMES	*plantago*
RANGE	throughout the Southwest
USES	food, medicine

$38 \cdot$ Prickly Pear Cactus
Opuntia spp.

Prickly pears, native to the Americas, are now common in warmer climates throughout the world. Humans semi-domesticated the prickly pear centuries ago in Mexico and Peru, where large orchards are planted for *tunas* (fruits) and the young *pencas* (pads), called *nopales*—the Spanish name for the plant. The fruits and pads are important sources of vitamins A and C. The pads are also high in mucilage and have become an effective remedy for lowering blood pressure and cholesterol levels.

C. Allan Morgan

Most species of prickly pear have edible fruits and pads, but not all species are equally attractive, tasty, and kind to the collector. The most common and popular in the Southwest is *O. engelmannii*, which has very round pads. The fruits are laden with tiny spines called *glochids* that are more felt than seen, so care must be taken when harvesting them. Rubbing or vigorously brushing the fruits usually removes these insidious armaments, but using tongs to pick the fruits is a safer bet. Many people still boil the pulp and make it into prickly pear jelly or candy. The pads must be harvested young to be edible.

Prickly pears have long been an important source of a bright purple to reddish dye called *cochineal*. The source of this potent pigment is the larva of a scale insect (*Dactylopius coccus*) that wraps itself into a cocoon of white silk on prickly pear pads. The cocoons often appear on pads as dirty white masses of tissue. Native peoples of central Mexico discovered many centuries ago that the larvae when squashed produce a colorfast dye. Cochineal is still produced today in Mexico and Peru.

Adobe workers boil *pencas* and add the liquid to plaster to make it adhere to adobe.

FAMILY	Cactaceae
OTHER NAMES	*nopal*
RANGE	throughout the Southwest
USES	food, dye

Ratany is a nondescript, smallish shrub of southwestern valleys and gentle hillsides. The plants sport bright though tiny magenta flowers and inedible fruits clad in abundant though harmless spines. The leaves are few and very small. Ratany may grow as a root parasite on adjacent plants. In times of drought it loses its leaves and resembles only an organized pile of twigs.

Indigenous peoples found the plants, especially the roots, to be of multiple uses, and many people even today maintain a supply of the dried roots and stems in their homes. Medicinally, the roots, ground up or brewed into an infusion, are thought to heal sores and bruises. Tea brewed from the roots is a popular remedy for diabetes. An infusion of flowers and stems is widely reputed to help cure digestive ailments.

The roots, when pounded and boiled, are a source of a powerful red pigment useful for dyeing fabric and leather. The same decoction also acts as a fixative and color enhancer for other dyes.

Bruce Griffin

FAMILY	Krameriaceae
OTHER NAMES	*tajui*
RANGE	throughout the Southwest
USES	medicine, dye

40 · Saguaro
Carnegiea gigantea

FAMILY	Cactaceae
OTHER NAMES	*saguo*
RANGE	Arizona, California, northern Mexico
USES	food, wood

The saguaro is not only one of the most iconic plants of the Southwest, but was also one of the most important food plants for desert peoples. The great cactus played such a key role in their survival that the Tohono O'odham based their annual calendar on its reproductive cycle.

The tips of mature saguaro branches become crowded with large buds in April. The showy white flowers, usually 3 inches across, open at night and are pollinated by a variety of opportunists, especially bats. The reddish fruits ripen mostly between mid-June and mid-July. The waxy rinds split open, exposing the sweet and tasty pulp, which has the texture of a dried fig. The fruits that animals do not consume fall to the ground at just about the time when summer rains usually begin, ensuring that the seeds will germinate. For desert peoples, the fruits were a dietary basic. They also formerly gathered many fruits together and squeezed out the juice, allowing it then to ferment into a mildly intoxicating wine. This they drank at an annual festival of celebration. This tradition continues today.

Saguaros may live as long as 250 years and have been measured at more than 60 feet tall. When they die, their green flesh and white pulp wither away, leaving behind a cylinder of woody ribs. Desert peoples put these long sticks to good use. For gathering saguaro fruits, a couple of ribs lashed together with a hook at the tip is the ideal tool. The ribs are still the preferred choice for the roofs of ramadas. They are strong enough to hold a layer of brush or other material on top, providing complete shade from the desert sun.

C. Allan Morgan

41 · Sandfood
Pholisma sonorae

This is a sensational plant that most people will never see, even those who frequent its habitat—the very dry deserts of the Southwest. It is a wholly parasitic plant, dependent for its very existence on other desert plants, and ekes out its living only in sandy soil, including active and stabilized sand dunes. Most of the plant's bulk lies below the surface, and during dry seasons (which is most of the time in its habitat) the plant shrinks to almost nothing. The buried stems, which resemble roots, may penetrate 5 feet deep into the soil. Unless one is deliberately seeking the plant, it is easy to pass right next to the mushroom-like aboveground portion and never notice it. Some Native Americans can locate the plants when they are practically invisible to outsiders.

Sandfood ("dune tuber," as its Spanish name is translated) is well named, for it is probably the best food source in the sand country of the great, dry, empty deserts of the Southwest. Native Americans and travelers alike came to rely on the plant for

Bruce Griffin

food and liquid, and their survival may have turned on their ability to locate plants suitable for consumption. The edible portion lies underground and must be dug up. I have not tasted it, but many accounts describe it as having a delicate flavor and texture, a gourmet delight. Very little is known about the biology of the plants, for they seem largely to disappear once their hosts become water stressed. They appear to inflict no harm whatsoever on the plants on which they are parasitic, and may even render the hosts healthier and more robust. A distressing percentage of their original habitat has been cleared for agriculture, but much still remains intact.

FAMILY	Lennoaceae
OTHER NAMES	*camote de los médanos*
RANGE	Arizona, California, northern Mexico
USES	food

42 · Saya
Amoreuxia palmatifida

Far too few people have an opportunity to see and taste sayas. Unless you look for them during or immediately after the summer rains, you may never find them, even where they are common. The aboveground portion of the plant sprouts with summer rains, matures, flowers, fruits, and then shrivels away, and only the underground tuber is left, well hidden from marauders, its existence known only to a few successful javelinas.

Sayas are nifty plants. Their leaves are deeply lobed, bright green, and large; their flowers yellow to golden, conspicuous, and showy. The fruits are small capsules and the seeds are black. Leaves, flowers, fruits, and seeds are edible. When the seeds age, they become hard and round, like tiny hard rubber balls. The roots, however, are the best source of food. They are tuberous and are tasty raw or roasted. The tubers form a complex underground network, and even though they may be excavated, the following year new plants will sprout from roughly the same place.

Bruce Griffin

FAMILY	Bixaceae
OTHER NAMES	Mexican yellowshow
RANGE	Arizona, New Mexico, Texas, northern Mexico
USES	food

43 · Seepwillow
Baccharis salicifolia

A long the few desert streams in the Southwest that remain in their natural state, a characteristic riparian odor can be detected, especially after runoff from summer storms. This rather agreeable scent comes from the seepwillow, a plant especially well adapted to survive flooding. Although its branches may exceed 10 feet in height, they are resilient and accept the weight of torrents of water gracefully, springing back as the waters ebb. The leaves resemble those of willows; hence the scientific name *salicifolia*, which means "willow leaf."

The straight, supple branches supplied indigenous people with shafts for arrows. While that use is archaic, another is still current. The leaves seem to possess the unusual property of absorbing odors. For people with smelly feet, a few leaves placed in the shoe and left there while the shoe is worn seem to neutralize the odor, an inexpensive remedy for an embarrassing problem. The branches, leaves, and roots, when pounded, give off a foamy substance that seems to overcome body odor.

Seepwillow leaves may have contraceptive properties, according to some natives. A tea brewed from the leaves may aid in this endeavor and provide general benefits for a woman's reproductive cycle. The branches can easily be woven into a roof and siding for a temporary shelter.

Rick and Nora Bowers

FAMILY	Asteraceae
OTHER NAMES	mule's fat, *batamote*
RANGE	throughout the Southwest
USES	tools, medicine, building

44 · Sotol
Dasylirion wheeleri

FAMILY	Agavaceae
OTHER NAMES	desert spoon
RANGE	Arizona, New Mexico, Texas, northern Mexico
USES	food, beverage, fiber

This yucca-like relative of the agave grows in the higher parts of the southwestern deserts, often in association with junipers and low-elevation oaks. It is also known as *desert spoon* because its wide leaves have spoonlike depressions when they are extracted from the dead base. Its flowering shoot is rather flimsier than the stalk of yuccas, agaves, or beargrass, and the flower panicle is much more compact. The plants are rather slow-growing and deserve protection for their beauty and for the number of animal species they harbor among their leaves.

The fruits and flowers are both edible when cooked, though few people now eat them. The youthful flowering shoot seems to have had the most flavor. The leaves, which are an inch or more wide, were an important source of fiber for weaving a variety of mats and coarse baskets. The most interesting product is a distilled liquor called, oddly enough, *sotol*, bottled and sold commercially in Chihuahua, Mexico. An acquaintance of mine related many years ago that he had imbibed a product called *sotol de víbora* (rattlesnake sotol) that contained an entire rattlesnake embalmed in the jug. He claimed even a small dose produced a tingling sensation in his fingertips and toes. Others report that sotol is clearly inferior to tequila.

C. Allan Morgan

45 · Sumac
Rhus trilobata

FAMILY	Anacardiaceae
OTHER NAMES	squawbush, lemonade bush, *aigritas*
RANGE	throughout the Southwest
USES	food, beverage, tools, tannins, dye, medicine

This relative of poison ivy is probably the most popular native plant used for making nonalcoholic beverages. It might well be considered the coffee, tea, and soda pop plant of the Southwest. A plant of the chaparral, with cousins growing in the higher mountains and below in the deserts, some sumacs also go by the name lemonade bush, a dead giveaway to its delightful properties. The bushes may reach 8 feet in height. The currant-size dark red fruits have a sweet-sour taste: a sweet, almost sugary, outer coating, and a tart interior. Native peoples throughout the region have discovered that smashing the berries, or grinding them on a stone *metate*, and adding the mass to water yields a most refreshing drink. The berries can be harvested when ripe and stored, then ground when the appropriate occasion arises. The wiry branches proved useful in binding and in manufacturing implements and are still used in making baskets and other wares. The branches contain tannin used in producing dyes. The fruits are a source of pigments and also have broad medicinal properties.

Some species of sumacs are dioecious, hence many of the plants are male and yield no berries. In fall the leaves often turn red, offering an autumn display.

46 · Sunflower
Helianthus annuus

FAMILY	Asteraceae
OTHER NAMES	*girasol*
RANGE	throughout the Southwest
USES	food, dye, medicine

In years when summer rains have been abundant, roadsides and pastures of the Southwest often become overrun with sunflowers that seem to illuminate the landscape. With generous moisture, the plants may reach 10 feet in height. They benefit from human activity, thriving in disturbed soils and relishing the runoff moisture along roads. With their brilliant yellow ray flowers and dark brown disk, they are among the easiest southwestern plants to identify. Some people consider them weeds, since livestock will not touch them and the leaves give off an unpleasant smell when crushed. They are useful weeds, however, primarily due to the abundant seeds.

Indians of the Southwest long ago made sunflower seeds an important part of their diet. (Sunflowers originated in the Americas and their domesticated descendants are grown throughout the world.) The process of separating the achenes (kernels) from the seeds is difficult and labor intensive. When the seed heads dry out thoroughly and are beaten, the seeds drop out. Beating the seeds themselves exposes the edible kernel, which remains behind when the mass is winnowed. The kernels are so oily that they are used to season griddles, but they are also nutritious and, as most of us know, tasty. When ground into meal they can be soaked in water to make *pinole,* or grain-based porridge. The meal, when thoroughly ground, may take on the consistency of peanut butter and can be eaten by itself or added to other ground seeds and made into cakes that are tasty and store well.

Some native peoples also found the seed coats to be a valuable source of dyes in an array of vibrant colors. Others found the plants a source of a variety of medicines, especially effective for treating infections and, oddly enough, warts.

C. Allan Morgan

47 · Walnut
Juglans major

Rick and Nora Bowers

I lived for several years in a deep canyon in the Chiricahua Mountains of southeastern Arizona. Behind my cabin was a huge walnut tree that served as a protective canopy for my automobile and other equipment. Each year I would test the walnuts and wonder at the dedication of people who could gain nourishment from them. The shells are difficult to extract from the husks and are very hard. If one cracks a nut with a stone, as native peoples frequently did, the blow usually crushes most of the meat, which is of very strong flavor anyway.

I was forgetting, however, that native peoples needed to exploit every possible food resource, and walnuts were one. Mountain indigenous peoples discovered that mixing the meat with roasted mescal yielded a satisfying sweet that was worth all the effort of smashing the husks and cracking the nuts.

Although walnuts are trees of mountain canyons, they will frequently survive well at lower elevations along watercourses that connect with the mountains. Thus, they were accessible to people who lived at the edge of the desert. I have not discovered any records of the use of the wood by native peoples, despite the fact that it has many of the attributes of fine eastern walnut.

FAMILY	Juglandaceae
OTHER NAMES	*nogal*
RANGE	Arizona, New Mexico, Texas, Utah, northern Mexico
USES	food

48 · Willow
Salix gooddingii

FAMILY	Salicaceae
OTHER NAMES	Goodding willow, *sauce*, *saúz*
RANGE	throughout the Southwest
USES	medicine, building, fiber, tools

Willows grow in great thickets, or *bosques*, along southwestern rivers and streams. They withstand most floods, and seeds sprout rapidly after flooding. A cutting of a branch stuck in moist ground will sprout roots and leaf out quickly.

Willow numbers have plummeted nearly everywhere due to the lowering of water tables by excessive pumping, mechanical destruction of streamside habitats, and the invasion of the exotic tamarisk, or salt cedar, tree. Willow *bosques* are vitally important bird habitats for many species, including the endangered southwestern willow flycatcher. The dense forests can also provide a haven for mammals, especially deer.

Willows are the natural source of acetylsalicylic acid, or aspirin. Indigenous peoples throughout North America discovered centuries ago that chewing on willow bark could reduce fever and pain. Not all willows produce the same amounts of aspirin, but Goodding willow apparently produces enough to make its bark an effective source of the palliative.

In addition to willow's medicinal virtues, its supple and flexible branches can be easily woven. Indigenous people used the branches in weaving hats and baskets, in construction of shelters, and in diversion weirs, essential for channeling irrigation water to crops. Farmers along southwestern streams learned long ago to plant rows of cuttings to form woven fences, a means of reclaiming farmland lost to streamside erosion. Today many rows of large willows and cottonwoods bear testimony to the effectiveness of the technique.

Rick and Nora Bowers

C. Allan Morgan

Four species of wolfberries in the Southwest produce edible berries. Their fruits are attractive, the red or orange berries contrasting most agreeably with the green and gray of the bushes and the general browns of the desert. The fruiting season has great variability, so much so that at any given time one is liable to find ripe wolfberries. Some years none may appear.

Roughly the size of a pea, the berries vary greatly in sweetness and juiciness; however, their quality was sufficiently reliable that numerous peoples of the Southwest came to depend on them. The berries are often tasty when eaten off the bush, but also preserve well, being amenable to sun-drying and storage for extended periods. Native peoples mashed and ground the dried fruits, incorporating the residue into flour and as a beverage base. Not all peoples found wolfberries to their liking, perhaps a reflection of either regional variation of the plants or the relative abundance of more succulent fruits.

Indigenous peoples of the Southwest also found many uses for other parts of the plant. Leaves and roots were used to dull pain, and ceremonial uses have been recorded as well.

FAMILY	Solanaceae
OTHER NAMES	*bachata*
RANGE	throughout the Southwest
USES	food, beverage, medicine, ceremony

50 · Yucca
Yucca arizonica, Spanish dagger
Yucca baccata, Banana yucca
Yucca elata, Soaptree yucca
Yucca brevifolia, Joshua tree

Tom Bean

A friend and I once found ourselves camping in a desert flat in the vicinity of a grove of banana yuccas. We had both heard that the fruits were edible, and these plants had what appeared to be succulent young fruits, shaped rather like small unripe bananas. Rather than go hog wild with a fruit rumored to have a laxative effect, we harvested a couple and sautéed them in bacon fat along with an apple we happened to have with us. The result was a downright tasty dish that we consumed in moderation. Those who succumb to the taste of the fruits and eat too many will probably suffer soon from their rash indulgence. Native Americans of the Southwest made the fruits a staple of their diets. The fruits are not edible when too green, however, nor do they keep well after ripening, so the timing of the harvest is critical.

In addition to their importance as a food source, yuccas yield fiber that was essential for making rope and baskets. The soaptree yucca, as the name suggests, was a source of soap. Centuries ago indigenous peoples discovered that if they pounded the roots repeatedly with a heavy object, the mass would exude a bubbly liquid that could be used for washing clothes and people, including hair.

A moth that lives only in yuccas is responsible for pollinating them. The female moth collects pollen and deposits her eggs in the ovary of the fruit, pollinating it during the process. The larvae eat a portion of the seeds, but enough fertile seeds survive to ensure perpetuation of the yucca.

Like their cousins the agaves, yuccas are related to lilies. Joshua trees are the lilies of the Mojave Desert, though their range extends into the northwestern reaches of the Sonoran Desert where they intermingle with saguaros in a limited area. While they are prolific in parts of Arizona and Nevada, the vast majority grows in southern California. Whereas saguaros generally avoid frost-prone areas, Joshua trees require frost for their development. They are nearly as slow-growing as saguaros and may live for several hundred years, perhaps as long as 900. Once one has seen them in their habitat, it is difficult to confuse them with any other plant. As is the case with other yuccas, a larva that lives exclusively in the trees pollinates the flowers. Fallen branches are the nearly exclusive habitat for the smallest lizard in North America, the desert night lizard *(Xantusia vigilis)*.

For indigenous peoples of the Mojave Desert, Joshua trees were an important resource. The roots were a source of soap, while fiber from roots and leaves proved valuable for making cord, baskets, mats, sandals, and even clothing. With proper preparations, the flowers, fruits, and roots were all edible, perhaps even tasty. When roasted, the flowers have a sweet taste. The fruits can be boiled, then pressed into cakes and stored.

Unlike agaves, yuccas flower repeatedly throughout their lives—usually about every three years—continuing to live after sending up a flowering shoot.

Rick and Nora Bowers

C. Allan Morgan

FAMILY	Agavaceae
OTHER NAMES	*dátil*
RANGE	throughout the Southwest
USES	food, fiber, shelter, tools

SUGGESTED READING

Bowers, Janice Emily. *Shrubs and Trees of the Southwest Deserts.* Tucson: Western National Parks Association, 1993.

Dunmire, William, and Gail Tierney. *Wild Plants and Native Peoples of the Four Corners.* Santa Fe: Museum of New Mexico Press, 1997.

Felger, Richard. *Flora of the Gran Desierto.* Tucson: University of Arizona Press, 2000.

Felger, Richard, and Mary Beck Moser. *People of the Desert and Sea: Ethnobotany of the Seri Indians.* Tucson: University of Arizona Press, 1985.

Gentry, Howard Scott. *Agaves of Continental North America.* Tucson: University of Arizona Press, 1982.

Hodgson, Wendy. *Food Plants of the Sonoran Desert.* Tucson: University of Arizona Press, 2001.

Lumholtz, Carl. *New Trails in Mexico: An Account of One Year's Exploration in Northwestern Sonora, Mexico and Southwestern Arizona, 1909–1910.* New York: Scribner's, 1912.

Moore, Michael. *Medicinal Plants of the Desert and Canyon West.* Santa Fe: Museum of New Mexico Press, 1990.

Nabhan, Gary Paul. *Gathering the Desert.* Tucson: University of Arizona Press, 1985.

Niethammer, Carolyn. *American Indian Food and Lore.* New York: Macmillan, 1972.

Rea, Amadeo. *At the Desert's Green Edge: An Ethnobotany of the Gila River Pima.* Tucson: University of Arizona Press, 1993.

Turner, Ray, Janice Emily Bowers, and Tony Burgess. *Sonoran Desert Plants: An Ecological Atlas.* Tucson: University of Arizona Press, 1985.

Yetman, David, and Thomas R. Van Devender. *Mayo Ethnobotany: Land, History, and Traditional Knowledge in Northwest Mexico.* Berkeley: University of California Press, 2002.

INDEX

ABOUT THE AUTHOR

David Yetman is a nationally known author and host of the television series *The Desert Speaks*. A research social scientist at the Southwest Center of the University of Arizona, Dr. Yetman's most recent studies include the use of plants in northwest Mexico. He is the author of nine books, including the 2007 publication *The Great Cacti*, and numerous journal articles. After years of training as a philosopher and more than a decade as an elected public official, Yetman has become an enthusiastic interpreter of the connections between plants and people. He lives in Tucson surrounded by desert plants.